D1454505

MAURICIO NEGRO

COLOUR OF PEOPLE

COLOUR OF PEOPLE

First published in 2017 in Brazilian Portuguese under the title
Gente de Cor, Cor de Gente by FTD Educação, São Paulo, Brazil

This English edition first published in 2018 by
Little Island Books
7 Kenilworth Park
Dublin 6W
Ireland

ISBN: 978-1-912417-07-0

A British Library Cataloguing in Publication record for this book is available from the British Library

Printed in Poland by L&C Printing

Little Island receives financial assistance from the Arts Council/ An Chomhairle Ealaíon and the Arts Council of Northern Ireland

10 9 8 7 6 5 4 3 2 1

For Flora and Jasmine
and all the children who inspired me to create this book

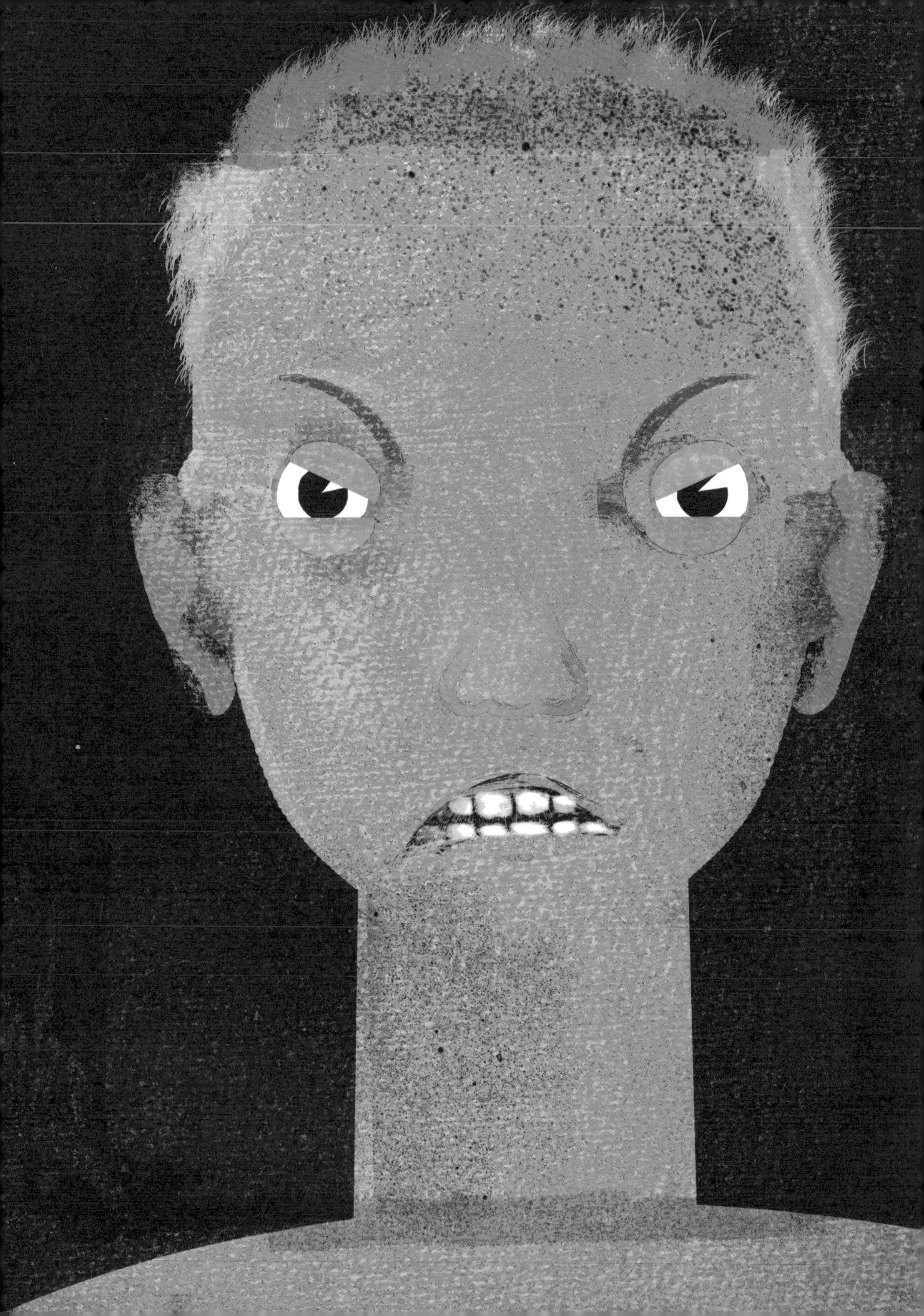

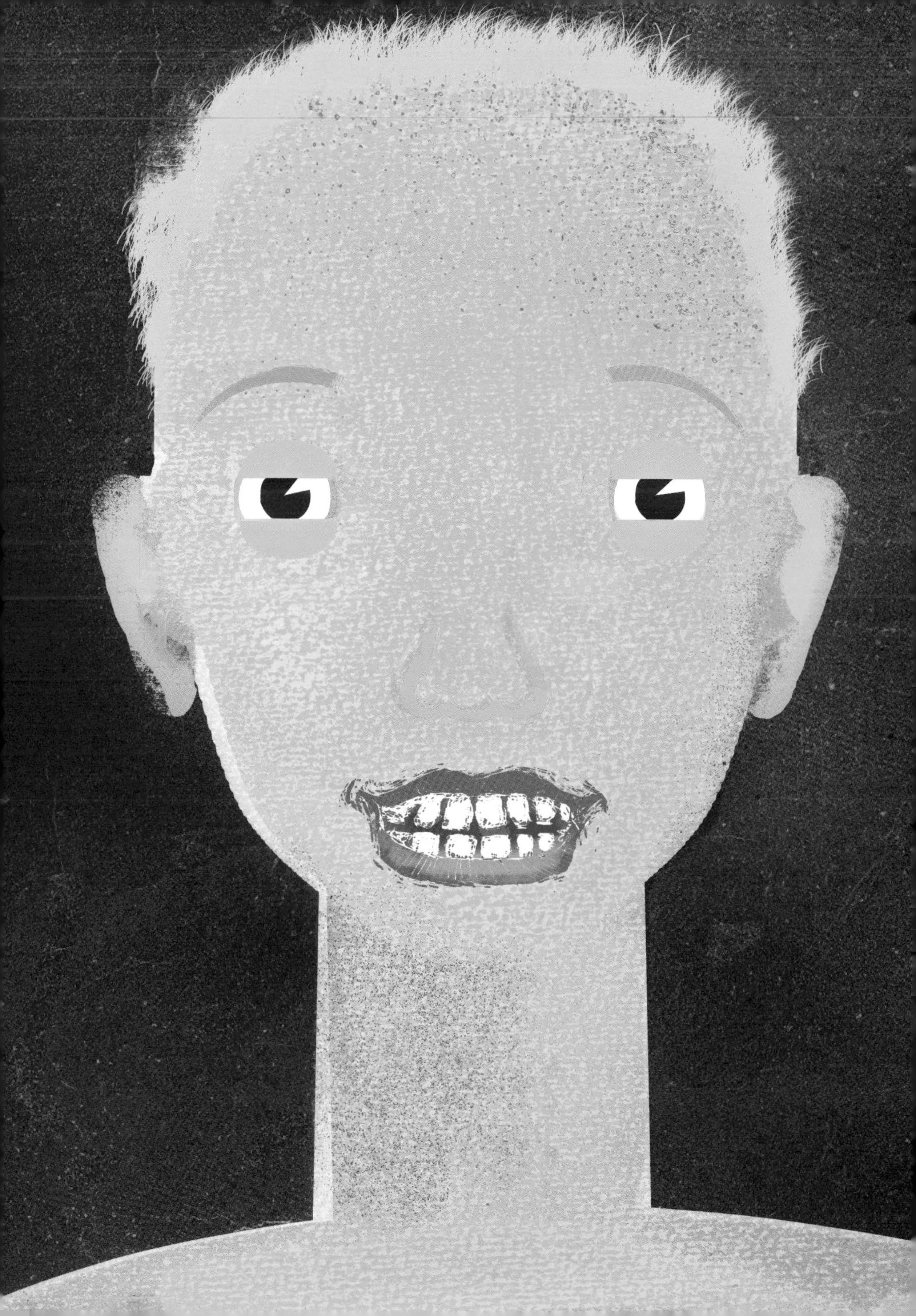

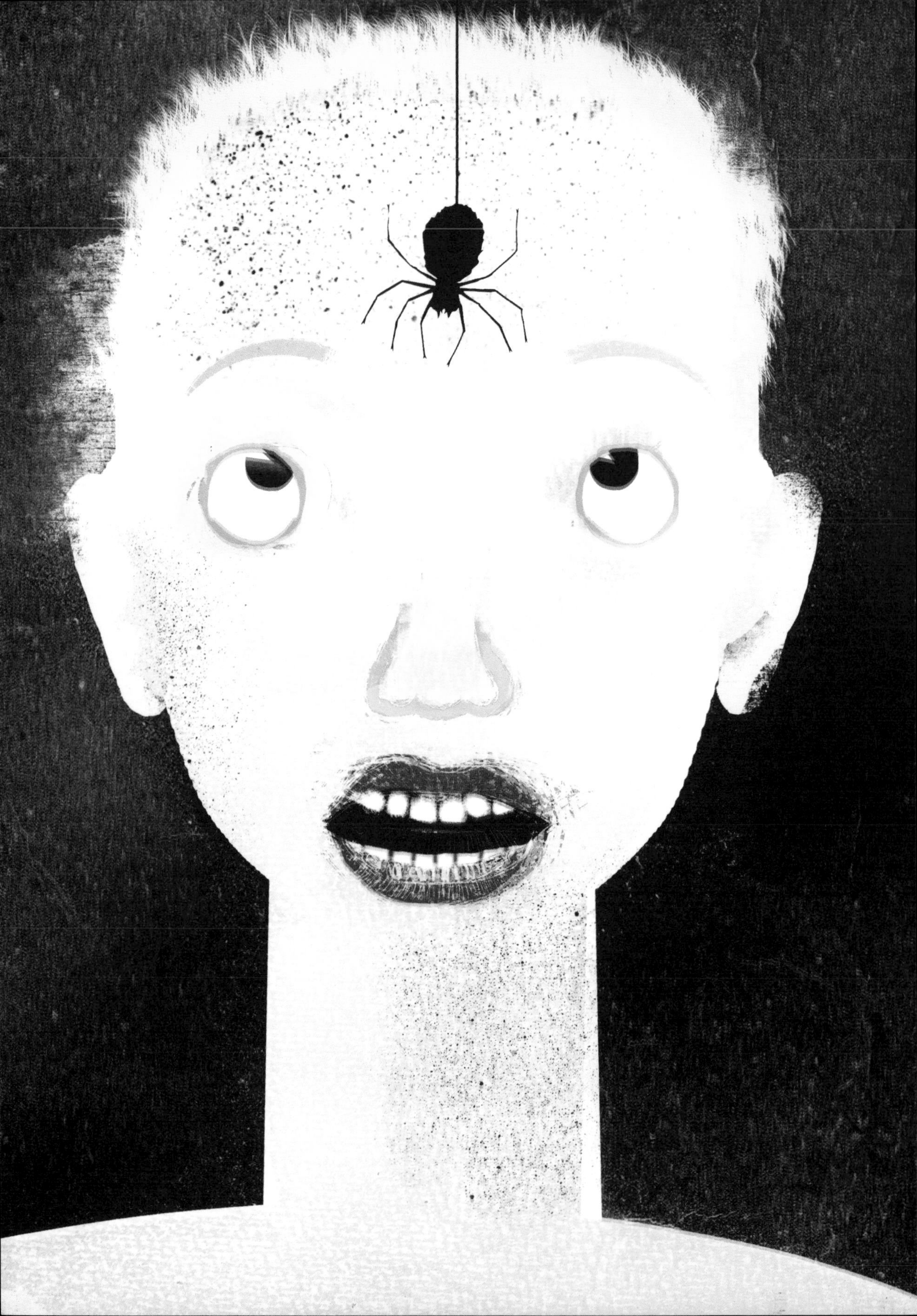

40°C

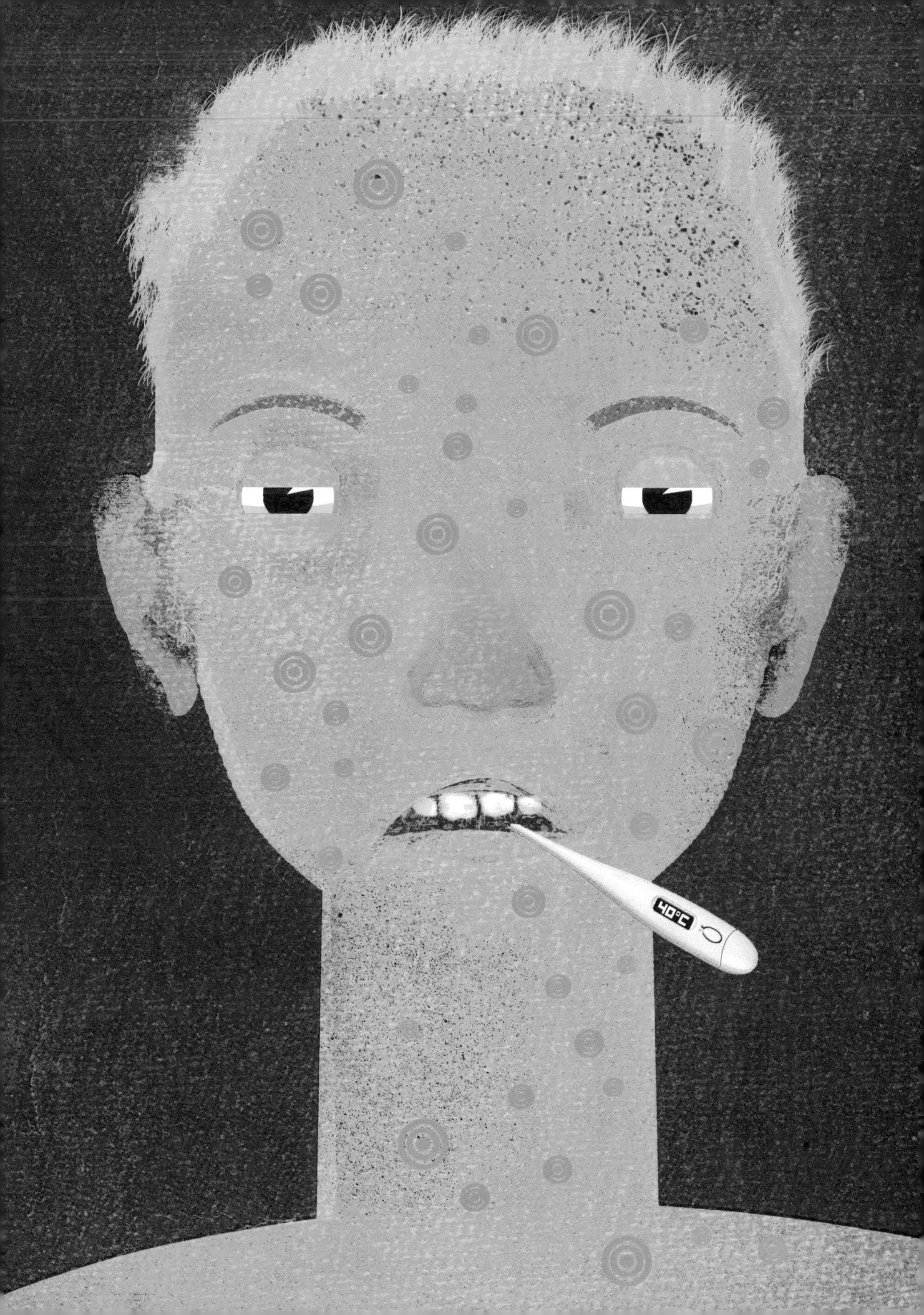
40°C

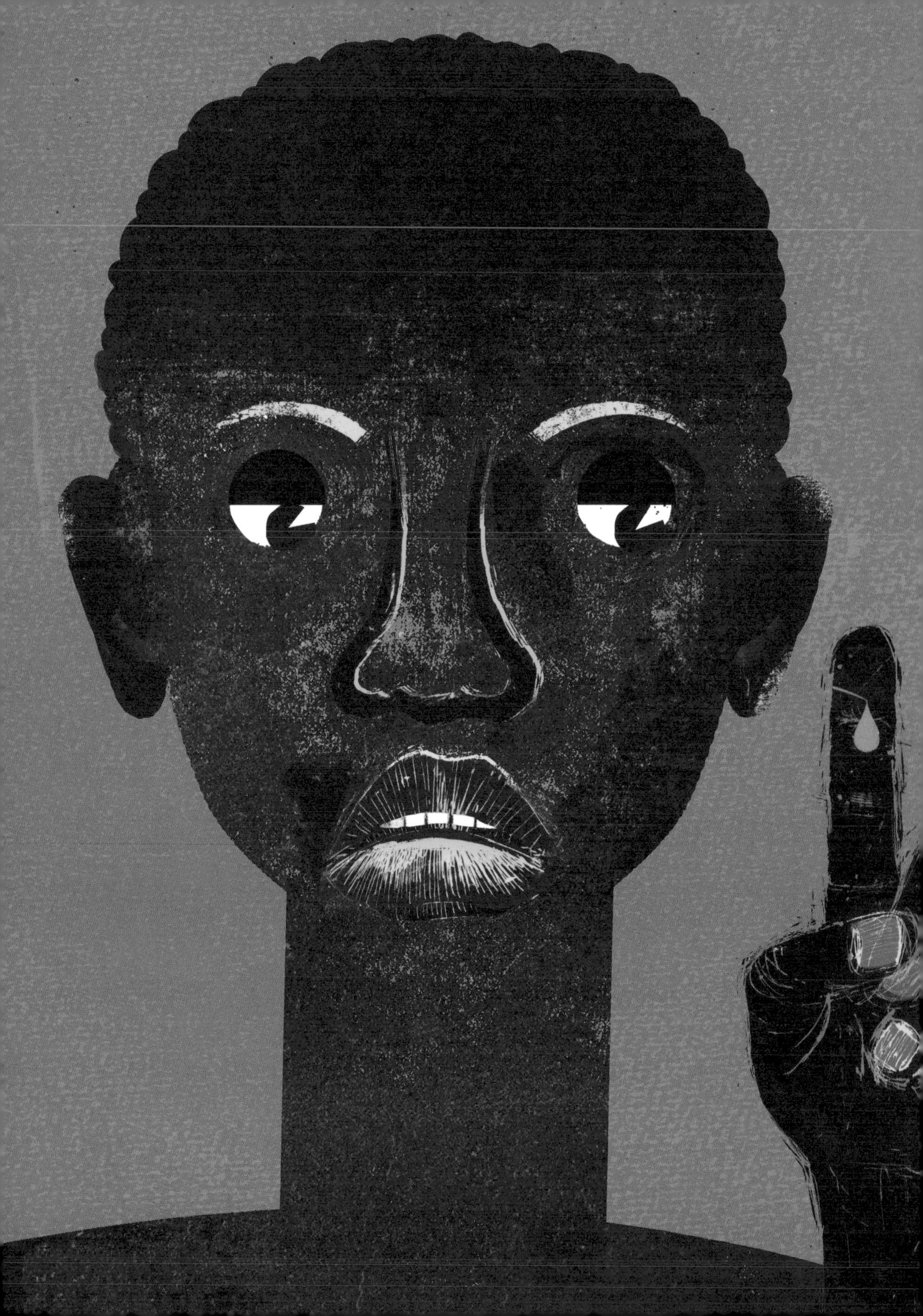

About the Author/Illustrator

Mauricio Negro is from São Paulo in Brazil. From an early age he loved reading books, and later became a writer, illustrator and graphic designer. He likes to work on projects to do with nature and Brazilian culture.

Mauricio is the author of several picture books and is a member of the board of directors of the Society of Illustrators of Brazil (Sociedade dos Ilustradores do Brasil). He has won numerous awards and participated in various exhibitions and events in Brazil and around the world.

About the Publisher

Based in Dublin, Little Island Books has been publishing books for children and teenagers since 2010. It is Ireland's only English-language publisher that publishes exclusively for young people. Little Island specialises in publishing new Irish writers and illustrators, and also has a commitment to publishing books in translation. This book was originally published in Brazil.